Printed and Published by D. C. THOMSON & CO., LTD., 185 Fleet Street, London EC.4A 2HS.

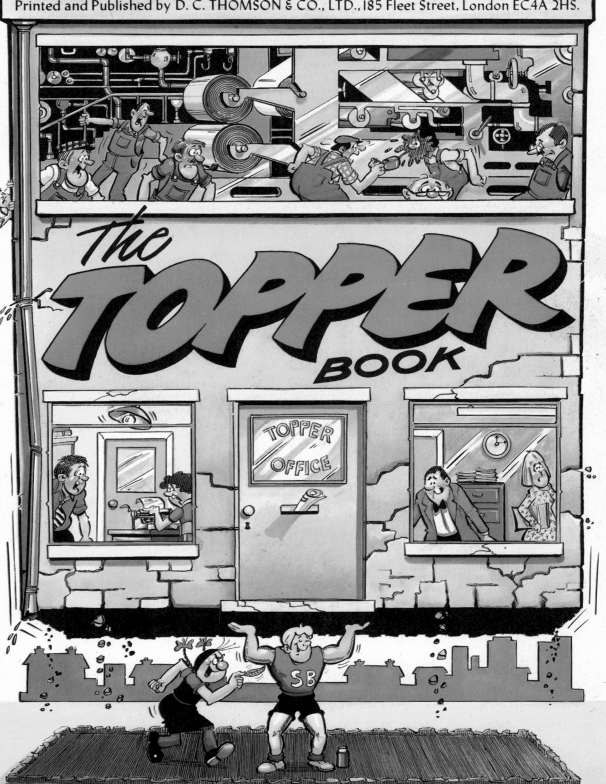

The greatest gagster of them all . . .

TRICKY DICKY

YIPPEE! ANOTHER DAY FULL OF TRICKS.

NO TRICKS TODAY, PLEASE. MUM AND I ARE BOTH GOING TO BE VERY BUSY WORKING AROUND THE HOUSE. WE WANT YOUR HELP FOR ONCE!

HEH! I CAN COMBINE BOTH.

PROD!

HERE! LET ME HELP, MUM! USE THIS NEW FEATHER DUSTER.

TA, DICKY.

GENUINE HEN FEATHERS, IT'S MADE FROM—OOPS! IT'S LAID AN EGG!

EEK!

CRACK!

SORRY ABOUT THAT, DAD. I CAN'T IMAGINE HOW IT HAPPENED. I'VE BROUGHT YOU A NEW BOX OF TACKS.

WIPE!

NAME John Chambers
ADDRESS 8 Dochfour Drive
Inverness
AGE

Fun when Dad whacks—some so-tricky tacks!

Dad's in for a scrub—from the rub-a-dub tub!

Dicky simply cannot stand—a helping of Dad's HELPING HAND!

Nick Kelly

SPECIAL AGENT

and CEDRIC HIS ASSISTANT

IN THE CASE OF THE

MYSTERIOUS MOLE

" Bleep! Bleep! Crack! " They're on the right track!

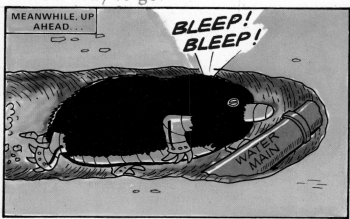

When Kelly's nearby—moles can fly!

She flies through the air with the greatest of " EEEEEEEEs!"

HUNGRY HORACE

ZULU KING

CHAKA THE TERRIBLE was the greatest Zulu warrior who ever lived. He was born in 1787, the son of a chief. His skill and boldness in battle soon earned him great fame and in 1816 he became leader of the Zulu tribe. Starting with an army of 500 untrained men, he set out to conquer the neighbouring tribes. Within four years he was king of a mighty Zulu empire, with an army of 100,000 warriors at his command.

Chaka was a magnificent figure of a man, six feet three inches tall. Here he is shown in his royal dress. His shield is of ox-hide, and he carries in his hand the short stabbing spear, or assegai, with which he armed his warriors.

Chaka was a splendid spear-thrower. As a herd boy, he practised with other boys by throwing his spear at a rolling ball. None of his rivals could match his skill at piercing the moving ball.

Once, when young Chaka was guarding cattle, a leopard attacked the herd. The leopard is said to be the fiercest and most dangerous of all wild animals, but Chaka did not desert his post. Armed only with spear and club, he killed the leopard.

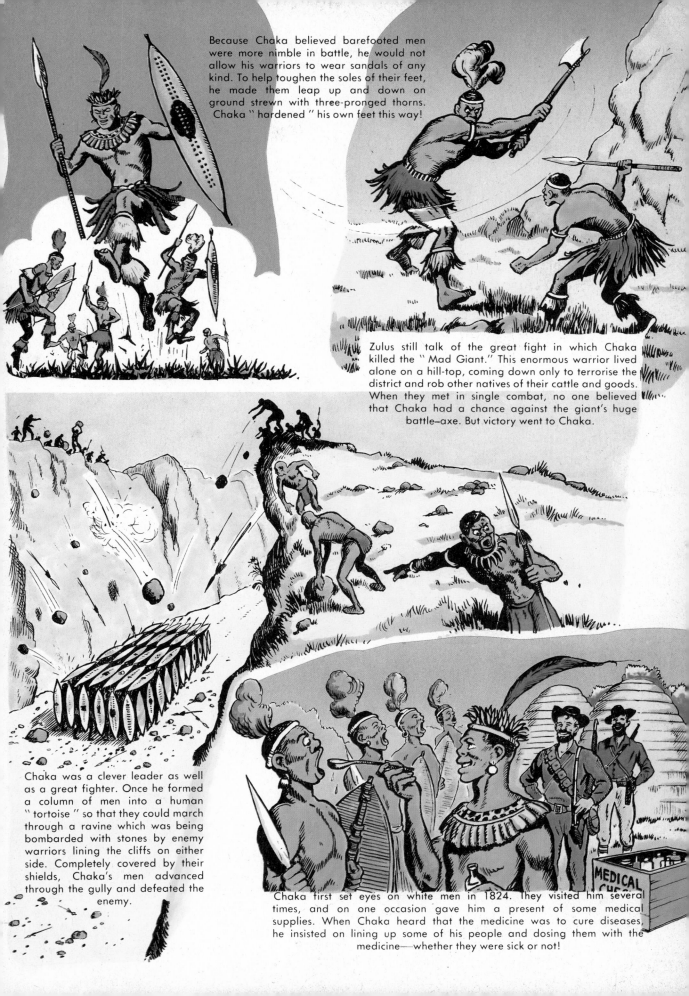

Because Chaka believed barefooted men were more nimble in battle, he would not allow his warriors to wear sandals of any kind. To help toughen the soles of their feet, he made them leap up and down on ground strewn with three-pronged thorns. Chaka "hardened" his own feet this way!

Zulus still talk of the great fight in which Chaka killed the "Mad Giant." This enormous warrior lived alone on a hill-top, coming down only to terrorise the district and rob other natives of their cattle and goods. When they met in single combat, no one believed that Chaka had a chance against the giant's huge battle-axe. But victory went to Chaka.

Chaka was a clever leader as well as a great fighter. Once he formed a column of men into a human "tortoise" so that they could march through a ravine which was being bombarded with stones by enemy warriors lining the cliffs on either side. Completely covered by their shields, Chaka's men advanced through the gully and defeated the enemy.

Chaka first set eyes on white men in 1824. They visited him several times, and on one occasion gave him a present of some medical supplies. When Chaka heard that the medicine was to cure diseases, he insisted on lining up some of his people and dosing them with the medicine—whether they were sick or not!

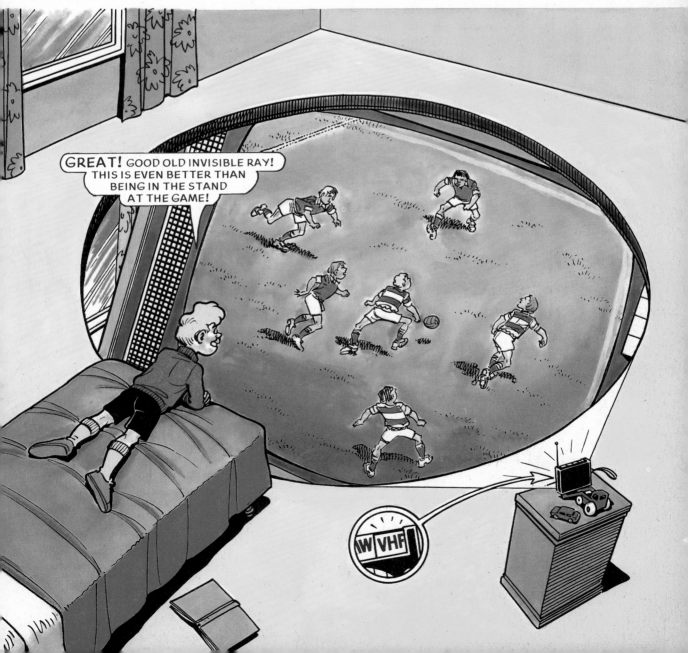

It's " plane " to see—they don't agree!

Jingo THE Jester

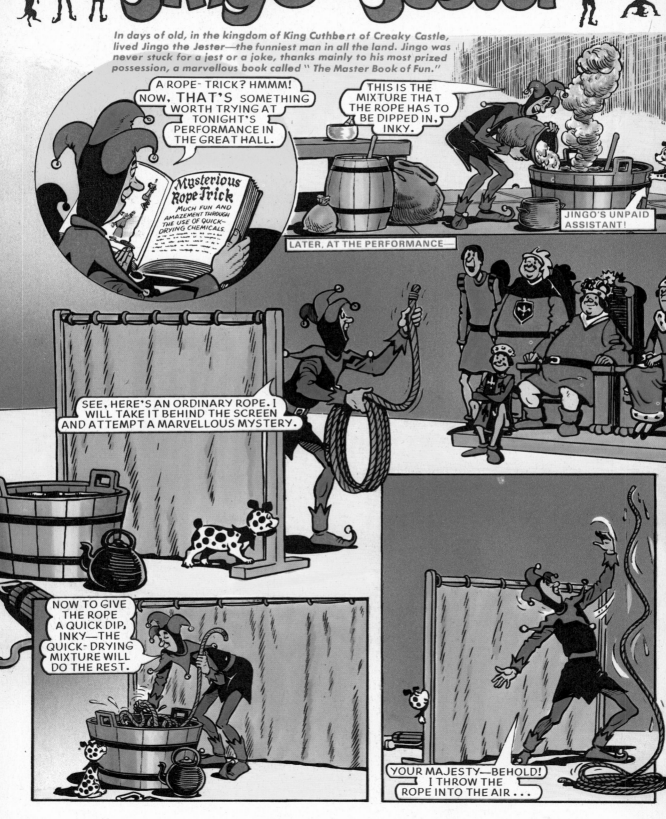

In days of old, in the kingdom of King Cuthbert of Creaky Castle, lived Jingo the Jester—the funniest man in all the land. Jingo was never stuck for a jest or a joke, thanks mainly to his most prized possession, a marvellous book called " The Master Book of Fun."

A ROPE- TRICK? HMMM! NOW, **THAT'S** SOMETHING WORTH TRYING AT TONIGHT'S PERFORMANCE IN THE GREAT HALL.

Mysterious Rope Trick MUCH FUN AND AMAZEMENT THROUGH THE USE OF QUICK— DRYING CHEMICALS.

THIS IS THE MIXTURE THAT THE ROPE HAS TO BE DIPPED IN, INKY.

JINGO'S UNPAID ASSISTANT!

LATER, AT THE PERFORMANCE—

SEE, HERE'S AN ORDINARY ROPE. I WILL TAKE IT BEHIND THE SCREEN AND ATTEMPT A MARVELLOUS MYSTERY.

NOW TO GIVE THE ROPE A QUICK DIP, INKY—THE QUICK- DRYING MIXTURE WILL DO THE REST.

YOUR MAJESTY—BEHOLD! I THROW THE ROPE INTO THE AIR . . .

Hoozee just can't cope—with being a microscope!

THINGUMMYBLOB

IN A LABORATORY EXPERIMENT THAT WENT WRONG, PROFESSOR T. POTT ACCIDENTALLY CREATED A "MONSTER." NOW HE'LL DO **ANY**THING TO GET RID OF IT!

EVERY DAY HE CLICKS THAT CALENDAR. AHA! THERE'S AN IDEA!

CLICK!

THAT'S THE EXPLOSIVE WIRED UP TO THE CALENDAR. WHEN HE CLICKS THAT BUTTON TOMORROW— BOOM!

NEXT DAY—

HUH! HE'S FORGOTTEN TO CHANGE THE CALENDAR!

ER—HAVE YOU SEEN THE DATE, PAL?

NO! IT'S NOT MY BIRTHDAY, YOU FOOL.

NO. IT'S NOT THE TV LICENCE RENEWAL DATE!

THE CALENDAR! CHANGE THE CALENDAR, YOU FOOL!

CLICK!

NO, IT'S NOT **YOUR** BIRTHDAY, EITHER!

THE CALENDAR, YOU TWIT! YOU'VE FORGOTTEN TO CHANGE THE CALENDAR! TAKE THAT!

BONK!

BOOM!

YES. THE CALENDAR! YES! UH-UH! YOU'VE GOT IT NOW. OH, GIMME STRENGTH!

CLICK!

GREAT GAMES

PALL ALL was a game popular with Indians long ago. Squares were marked on the ground, then the players kicked a flat stone from square to square while hopping on one leg. A sailor, who had been to India, introduced the game into Scotland where it became known as " Peevers ". Later, when English folk learned it, they called it ," Hop-Scotch ".

PELL MELL was a game once played regularly in Britain by nobles and other wealthy people. It was at the height of its popularity about the 17th century. There were special Pell Mell alleys, with raised banks at either end where hoops were set in the ground. The players used heavy mallets to strike a ball which had to pass through the hoop at the far side of the alley. The player who took fewest strokes to do this was the winner.

This picture shows the ancient game of NINEPINS being played in Egypt hundreds of years ago. The stone balls had to be rolled through the little arch, and the object of the game was to knock down the acorn-shaped " pins ". Slightly different forms of the game are still popular in many parts of the world at the present day.

BUFFETS was the name of this early form of boxing in England, and there are records of the sport dating from the 12th century. The rules were simple and skill wasn't needed—but toughness was! After deciding who was to have the first punch, the two contestants faced each other; then they struck alternate blows until one of them was knocked out!

The game of DOUBLE-BALL was a great favourite with North American Indians. It was played on a pitch which had goalposts at either end. The " ball " used was made from two cylinders of wood strung together with a length of rawhide. The players had tapered sticks with which they threw and caught the ball by means of the thong strung between two cylinders. A goal was scored when the ball was thrown in such a way that it hung across the crossbar of the opposing side's goalposts.

The game of TENNIS dates back many hundreds of years. A form of it is thought to have been played in Egypt and Persia more than 2000 years ago. In Britain in the Middle Ages it was a popular sport, played on special indoor courts. As you can see, the players used queerly-shaped rackets, and the " net " was only a length of rope hung a few feet above the ground.

BAITING THE BULL was a game played more than 800 years ago by soldiers on their way to the Crusades. The " bull " was an iron hook screwed high up in the wall of a room. A small ring hung from the ceiling on a long string, and the players had to throw it upwards, attempting to catch it on the hook.

STOOLBALL is a sport still played occasionally today. It is said to be the oldest game in England, dating from long before the Middle Ages. It is very much like cricket, but originally the wicket was simply a stool, and the " batsman " used only his hand to hit the ball. Later, roughly-made bats were introduced, and wooden boards fixed to posts became the wickets.

THE WHIZZERS FROM OZZ

One rainy day in Workchester, England, young Willie Walker wasn't feeling too happy.

BAH! I'M FED-UP! THERE'S NO FOOTBALL 'COS THE PITCH IS TOO SOGGY, AN' NOTHING EXCITING EVER HAPPENS IN WORKCHESTER . . .

Suddenly –

GREETINGS, EARTHLING!

YIKES! WH-WHAT—ER—WHO ARE YOU?

. . . TO OZZ! IT'S OUR PLANET'S TURN TO STAGE THE GALACTIC GAMES— AND WE'VE RESERVED THREE GRANDSTAND SEATS!

To Willie's amazement, the two green-skinned "things" removed their heads, to reveal two very special chums of his—Krik and Krak, twins from the far-off land of Whizz on planet Ozz, a planet of extremely advanced technology.

SURPRISE! HI, WILLIE!

WOWEE! A SORT OF SPACE OLYMPIC GAMES, EH?

WE THOUGHT YOU'D LIKE TO COME FOR A SPIN . . .

Excitement was high as the Galactic Games proceeded. Free from the threat of kidnapping—thanks to Willie and the Whizzer twins—the Ozz athletes gave a fantastic performance.

HOORAY FOR KLIML!

GOSH! WHAT A WEIRD CROWD!

KEEP GOING, GLIFFIP! DON'T LET PLANET PLINT DOWN!

C'MON, DROK! HOORAY FOR OZZ!

Later, after the team medals had been presented, there was one more ceremony to be carried out—

THE GALACTIC GAMES COMMITTEE OWES A GREAT DEBT TO YOU THREE. IT IS OUR WISH TO PRESENT YOU WITH THESE MEDALS.

PSST! WILLIE— SOON BE TIME TO GO HOME.

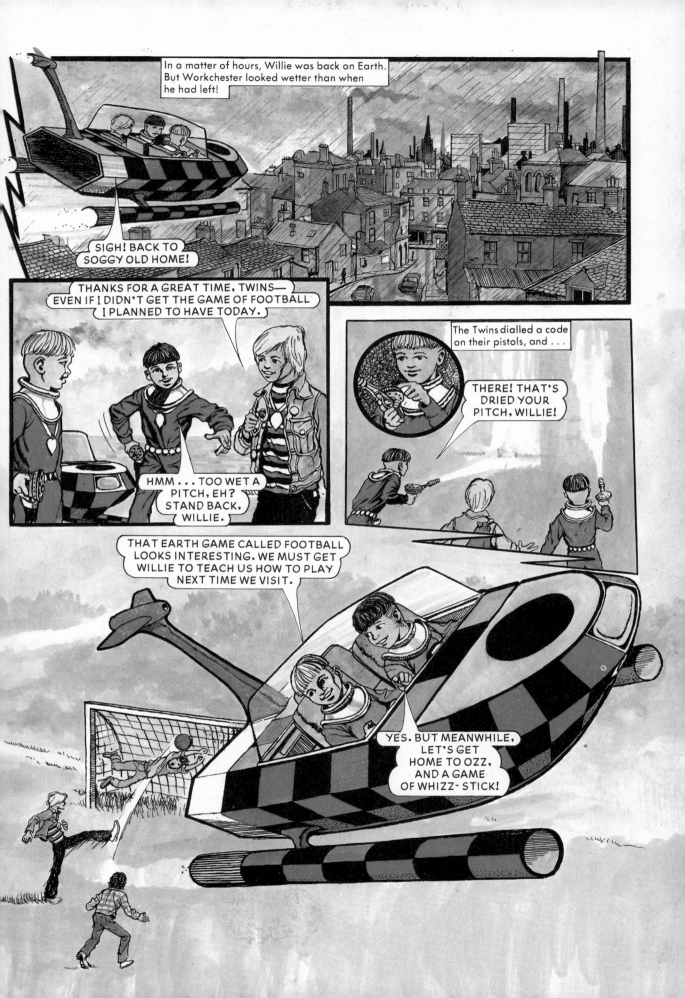

Yo-ho-ho! A-haunting we will go!

GHASTLY MANOR

I HOPE SOMEBODY BUYS THIS PLACE SOON—I CAN'T STAND IT MUCH LONGER!

FOR SALE

THIS IS MISTER FEAR. OWNER OF GHASTLY MANOR.

AH! SOMEONE AT THE DOOR. I HOPE IT'S A BUYER.

KNOCK! KNOCK!

HI, MAN! I'M MICKEY MACLAREN, THAT INCREDIBLY TALENTED SINGER, AND I'D LIKE TO BUY YOUR HOUSE.

YOU ARE? YOU WOULD?

SPLENDID! COME RIGHT IN!

HALLO! WE'LL SOON PUT A STOP TO THIS!

WOOOO!

WAH!

WOO!

GREAT! WHAT A SOUND! WE'LL SELL MILLIONS OF RECORDS!

CLATTER!

HERE YOU ARE, LADS—GRAB AN INSTRUMENT!

Screaming fans—crush Mr Fear's plans!

More gigglesome gags with . . .

TRICKY DICKY

I'VE GOT SOME SUPER TRICKS LINED UP TO TRY ON DAD TODAY. THEY'VE ALL GOT SOMETHING TO DO WITH BELLS!

AH! THE 'PHONE.

TRING! TRING!

HELLO!

YIKES!

HELLO! NICE TO MEET YOU. I'M YOUR TELEPHONE!

YEOWCH! YOU'VE DROPPED ME, YOU CLUMSY THING!

CRUMP!

Dad's position is tricky—till he's rescued by Dicky!

Little Baba's got—Ali tangled in a knot!

TRAIL-BLAZING

INTERESTING FACTS ABOUT EARLY MOTORING

IF, sometimes, crowded roads or fuel shortages make modern motoring none too easy, spare a thought for the hardy "trail-blazers" of the motoring age. They really had it tough!

Pity the boy who tried to steal a ride on this motor car! A row of small spikes were fixed to the flat back of some early cars to stop anyone from leaping on.

No, this motorist isn't off to the Arctic! The first cars had no windscreens or hoods, and drivers wore huge goatskin coats, goggles and peaked caps to protect themselves from the weather.

The first horseless carriages were powered by steam, and some of them achieved remarkable speeds. Unfortunately, the steam boilers were sometimes weak and exploded with disastrous results.

The bowler-hatted trumpeter isn't a street musician! This was the method used in the early days of Continental road-racing to give warning of the approach of a racing car.

Around 1890, many types of "horse-less carriage" were capable of speeds of about twenty miles an hour—but, by law, they had to be preceded by a man on foot carrying a red flag. And, until 1896, the speed was limited to two miles an hour in towns and villages, and four miles an hour in the country.

When old-time motorists saw a yellow ball hanging from a garage flag-pole, they knew that the local police were operating traps to catch speeding motorists. The signal was put up by the Automobile Association to assist their members.

Strange though it sounds, chemists used to stock the "cure" for motor cars that ran out of petrol! In the very early days of motoring, there were no garages or filling stations, and petrol was sold at chemists' shops.

At the beginning of this century, there were no floodlights to illuminate racing tracks. Roadmenders' lamps and flares were used to light the track at Brooklands in 1907 when S. F. Edge drove all through the night during a twenty-four hour record run. He averaged over sixty-five miles an hour.

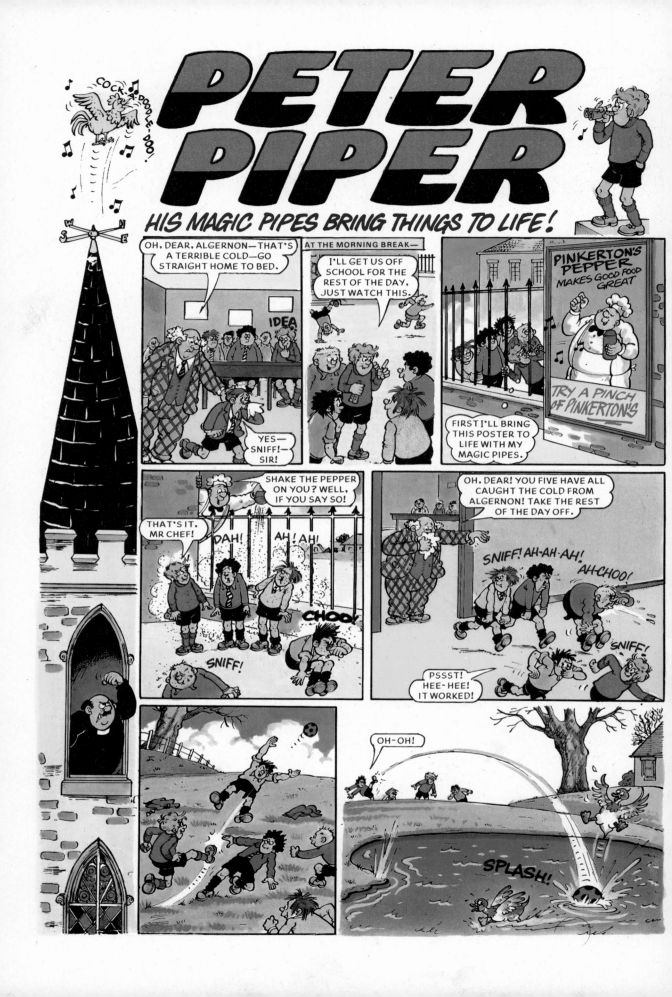

This'll take him aback—a ' stone ' having a snack!

HUNGRY HORACE

More, more, more—for Horace's winter store!

Nudge! Nudge! Wink! Wink! All's not quite as you think!

There's a big surprise due. Meet 'Cedric' Number Two!

When Kelly falls down—that jester looks a clown!

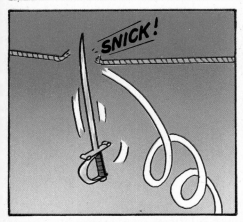

Souper Boy

Sidney's muscles really droop—

SIDNEY BRAITHWAITE

SO YOU'RE HAVING A BIRTHDAY PARTY, ARE YOU, SIDNEY? THAT'LL BE EXPENSIVE!

NOT AT ALL, DEAR. I'LL BE MAKING ALL THE FOOD.

SIDNEY'S BIRTHDAY—

A PRESSIE FOR YOU, SID...

COO! TA, ALFIE. I'LL OPEN IT AS SOON AS I GET THE PAPER OFF THIS ONE—

TOUGH PAPER, THIS. BUT A SWIG OF SOUPER SOUP WILL HELP.

POW!

ZAP!

THERE! IT'S EASY FOR SOUPER BOY.

R-RIP!

OOPS! COULDN'T STOP!

SMASH!

SIDNEY! CLUMSY ASS!

WHY DON'T YOU OPEN THE REST OF YOUR PARCELS OUTSIDE? THAT'LL BE SAFER.

RIGHT, DAD.

LET'S PLAY 'BLIND-MAN'S BUFF'! YOU CAN BE 'OUT' FIRST, SIDNEY!

SURE THING.

—until he drinks some souper-soup!

FREDDIE STARE

ZAP! ZAP! ZAP! ZAP! ZAP! ZAP!

THE PUPPET WITH EYES THAT HYPNOTISE!

I BET YOU LOT WISH YOU HAD A PUPPET LIKE FREDDIE —HE'S GREAT!

ANDY DUFF, FREDDIE'S OWNER

LATER, IN CLASS—

BLAH! BLAH! DRONE...

MISS BATT

WATCH THIS, FOLKS.

MAKE MISS BATT THINK SHE'S ME, FREDDIE.

ZAP!

SO—

HAR! LET'S HAVE AN INK-PELLET FIGHT, PALS!

SPRING!

MAKE THAT CHEEKY LITTLE TWIT THINK HE'S A HORSE IN THE GRAND NATIONAL!

N-NO, FREDDIE!

ZAP!

HUP! AND OVER THE NEXT FENCE!

SPACE

SPRING!

HAW! HAW!

HOO! HOO!

MEN OF MEXICO

THE Aztecs were a highly-skilled and warlike race who lived in Mexico hundreds of years ago. Among their number were great architects and engineers, who planned the wonderful cities and temples which so astonished the Spaniards who invaded Mexico in the 16th century.

The Aztecs were strong and wiry and men were able to carry tremendous loads. The loads were carried on a framework held in position on the bearer's back by a "tumpline," a band which passed over the forehead.

Many of the larger houses and temples of the Aztecs were beautifully constructed from giant blocks of cut stone. Here you see the construction of a temple, where the huge stone blocks are being dragged up a ramp over wooden rollers by scores of men. The work of erecting some of the great pyramid-like temples went on for many years.

The favourite sport of the Aztecs was "tlachtli." This game was played in a two-walled courtyard where a stone ring was fixed high up on each wall. The object of the game was to knock a solid rubber ball through the ring in the wall defended by the opponents. Players could use their knees, elbows and hips for striking the ball, but not their heads or feet.

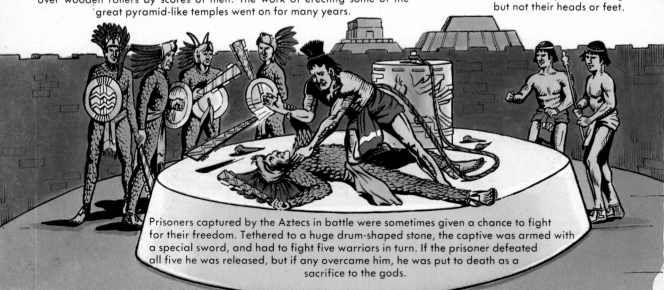

Prisoners captured by the Aztecs in battle were sometimes given a chance to fight for their freedom. Tethered to a huge drum-shaped stone, the captive was armed with a special sword, and had to fight five warriors in turn. If the prisoner defeated all five he was released, but if any overcame him, he was put to death as a sacrifice to the gods.